CONTENTS

KU-327-129

TRUCK RACING

Have you ever seen an **articulated lorry** barreling down the road? Can you imagine the sight of them racing each other? In the 1970s and 1980s, motor sports fans and drivers saw the potential for an exciting new sport. Truck racing was born. The thrill of seeing huge trucks battling at top speeds soon spread around the world.

Racing trucks were originally the same as **heavy goods vehicles (HGVs)**. This meant a driver could race in the same truck he had driven to the race. These days racing trucks are built for racing only.

When truck racing began, trucks raced at very high speeds. But the large trucks combined with high speeds resulted in dangerous and deadly accidents. Today truck racing has a speed limit. Trucks race at up to 161 kilometres (100 miles) per hour.

articulated lorry – a truck consisting of a cab and a trailer

heavy goods vehicle (HGV) – a large, heavy motor vehicle used for transporting goods

WILD MOMENTS OF
TRUCK RACING

BY M WEBER

Raintree is an imprint of Capstone Global Library Limited, a company incorporated in England and Wales having its registered office at 264 Banbury Road, Oxford, OX2 7DY – Registered company number: 6695582

www.raintree.co.uk
myorders@raintree.co.uk

Editorial Credits
Lauren Dupuis-Perez, editor; Sara Radka, designer; Laura Manthe, production specialist

ISBN 978-1-4747-4495-9 (paperback)
22 21 20 19 18 17
10 9 8 7 6 5 4 3 2 1

British Library Cataloguing in Publication Data
A full catalogue record for this book is available from the British Library.

Quote Sources
p.9, "Roger Decoster Interview, Covering 1971 thru 2001." Supercross, June 25, 2012; p.19, "Travis Pastrana Doubles up, Doubles Down." EPSN, April 28, 2014; p.22, "Connecting People Through News." PressReader.com, August 12, 2007

Acknowledgements
iStockphoto: GarysFRP, 10; Newscom: Cal Sport Media/Larry Clouse, 23, EPA, 8, Thomas Frey, 1, 25, Xinhua/ Zheng Huansong, 20, ZUMAPRESS/Hajek Ondrej/CTK, 26, 27, ZUMAPRESS/Panoramic, 29, ZUMAPRESS/ Wolfgang Fehrmann, 14, 16, 18, 19, Shutterstock: Action Sports Photography, 7, Art Konovalov, 11, Franck Boston, 13, Paul Drabot, 5; Wikimedia: Disconinja92, 21; graphic elements by Book Buddy Media

The publisher does not endorse products whose logos may appear on objects in images in this book.

Every effort has been made to contact copyright holders of material reproduced in this book. Any omissions will be rectified in subsequent printings if notice is given to the publisher.

All the Internet addresses (URLs) given in this book ... the dynamic nature of the Internet, some addresses ... to exist since publication. While the author and pub... responsibility for any such changes can be accepted ...

Truck racing is an exciting sport that is enjoyed around the world. Drivers train to handle these huge trucks at very high speeds.

CHAPTER 1

TRUCKS IN HOLLYWOOD

Truck racing in the United States began on 17 June 1979. The first race took place at the Atlanta International Raceway. Eager fans filled the stands. Trucks lined up at the starting line. All round the track were Hollywood camera crews.

This wasn't just a truck race. It was also the opening scene for the movie *Smokey and the Bandit II*. As the trucks took off down the track, cameras caught all the action.

This race also saw the first truck racing crash. The driver lost control of his truck. It spun into the wall as other racers sped past. The bonnet of the truck was torn off, revealing the engine below. It rolled to a stop on the opposite side of the track. It is a scene that fans can relive every time they watch the movie.

From 1960 to 1990, the Atlanta Motor Speedway was known as the Atlanta International Raceway. The track is 2.5 km (1.54 miles) long.

WILD! Professional racing trucks weigh up to 5,443 kilograms (12,000 pounds). The cabs usually stand more than 2.4 metres (8 feet) tall.

CHAPTER 2

THROUGH THE SMOKE

Racing trucks have huge diesel engines. This allows the trucks to race at high speeds, though it often produces a great deal of smoke.

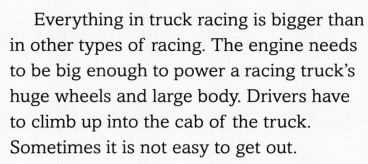

Everything in truck racing is bigger than in other types of racing. The engine needs to be big enough to power a racing truck's huge wheels and large body. Drivers have to climb up into the cab of the truck. Sometimes it is not easy to get out.

Bob Bolus learned this lesson during a 1984 race in Pennsylvania in the United States. When his truck experienced engine trouble, huge **plumes** of smoke poured into the cab. He tried to get out, but he couldn't see out the windows to tell which way was forwards. The truck spun sideways. Bolus couldn't stop the momentum of the enormous vehicle. The truck crashed into the wall. The smoke was so thick that fans could not see the truck. The wind created by other trucks racing past broke up the big cloud. When the truck came to a stop Bolus emerged unharmed, but out of the race.

plume – a long cloud of smoke or vapour resembling a feather

Racing trucks are equipped with a fire safety system. This allows drivers to respond and get out safely during an emergency.

TRUCK RACING IN THE UNITED STATES

The Great American Truck Racing Series existed in the 1970s and 1980s. It hosted all truck racing in the United States. The series was similar to other motor sport governing bodies. It set the rules for races. It also organized races and events. The series allowed trucks to race with speeds up to 249 km (155 miles) per hour. In 1988 this racing circuit went out of business. No organization has replaced it.

In 2015 an official truck racing series briefly returned to the United States. It was called ChampTruck. It unexpectedly ended in the middle of the season. Today the American truck racing circuit known as the Bandit Big Rig Series is hosting truck races across the country. It planned 11 events for the 2017 season.

CHAPTER 3

WHEELS IN THE AIR

Trucks can bump each other during races. Unlike some motor sports, truck racing crashes are less common. The size of the trucks keeps them driving ahead even when they get bumped. Crashes still happen, but they are rare.

A race in Jarama, Spain, in 2005 was the site of not one, but two crashes between racing trucks. In the first turn of the race, the lead trucks crashed into each other. This sent the other trucks spinning. One truck was pushed into a spin that ended with metal parts flying into the air.

Two minutes later the trucks went into the second turn. This time Manuel Gozalo lost control of his truck. It ploughed into the gravel, tipped sideways and turned upside down. Rescue crews rushed to the crash site. They rescued the driver from the wrecked truck. He walked away with minor injuries from one of the craziest crashes many fans had ever seen.

WILD!

The rules of the British Truck Racing Association (BTRA) allow "supplementary accessories which do not affect the performance or the handling of the vehicle". This includes fun accessories such as whistles and air horns!

Jarama is a racetrack near Madrid, Spain. It has held professional truck races since 1987.

CHAPTER 4

THROUGH THE BARRIERS

Safety measures for truck races include traps full of soft materials. These traps usually contain gravel and are meant to slow down a truck that is off the track.

At 13.5 km (8.4 miles), the racetrack in Le Mans, France, is one of the longest in the world. It hosts European truck races every year.

Drivers prepare carefully for every race. The truck is **inspected**. Safety requirements are checked. But sometimes trucks still break down.

In 2012 Brazilian driver Diumar Bueno took his truck for a practice run. He was driving 190 km (118 miles) per hour at the end of a long straight stretch. Bueno was approaching a turn when he suddenly realized that the brakes on his truck were not working. Bueno steered his truck towards the **infield** to try to slow down and avoid hitting the wall. The speed combined with the uneven ground caused his truck to soar into the air! He was unable to stop, and the truck crossed over the track again. He burst through the barriers. The truck fell headfirst down a hill that dropped 15.2 m (50 feet). Bueno suffered two broken legs, but he survived the crash. His truck, however, never raced again.

inspect – to look at something carefully

infield – the area in the center of a racetrack oval

CHAPTER 5

FIRE EMERGENCY

Truck racing is considered a "no contact" sport. This means no intentional crashes are allowed. However, trucks still make contact when racing at close quarters.

Many parts must come together to make a racing truck, from the engine to the frame. These trucks reach high speeds. But all of these parts are threatened when something goes wrong.

Geraldo Piquet knew his truck was in danger when he flipped and caught fire. It happened during a race in Brazil in 2012. A truck in front of him slowed quickly. In order to avoid an accident Piquet had to swerve his truck. He rolled across the track. His truck caught fire. The leaping flames were a dramatic sight for the crowd. Piquet dislocated an elbow in the accident. Amazingly, he raced again just the next week.

Drivers and fans enjoy seeing what trucks can do outside of races, as well. This includes stunts and manoeuvres such as lifting wheels off the ground.

Afterwards Piquet said, "Actually, it was not even my most serious accident. This was a little more Hollywood, had the rollover, the fire, everything . . . " He also said that the crash would not change the way he raced.

TRUCKS IN EUROPE

The governing body of all auto racing in Europe is called the Fédération Internationale de l'Automobile (FIA). It oversees the European Truck Racing Championship (FIA ETRC). Drivers from across Europe compete in a system that awards points for winning races. At the end of a season the driver with the most points wins €2,000 (about £1,700). The driver is also awarded a trophy.

CHAPTER 6

WELCOME TO INDIA

Truck racing in India is overseen by both the FIA and the Federation of Motor Sports Clubs of India.

Fans across the world flock to motor sports events. As the demand for excitement increases, truck racing has expanded around the globe.

India's first truck race took place in 2014. The day was a celebration of the sport of truck racing. It was an exciting **debut** for drivers and fans in India. Large trucks rumbled to the starting line. Drivers came from many different countries to race in front of the cheering crowd. More than 25,000 fans packed the stands to watch the trucks take off. First-time spectators got the chance to see just what the trucks had to offer.

debut – a first showing

Stuart Oliver won the 2014 debut race in India. He said, "It was an amazing experience. The track is beautiful, and trucks were performing great. I am thrilled to have won the first ever truck racing championship in India, among the enthusiastic crowds who were cheering each time we drove past the grandstand."

Stuart Oliver has been named BTRA Champion 10 times.

In addition to the racing, there was a fashion show and music. A driver even performed a truck dance, showing off with **doughnuts** and **three-point turns** in a premier truck.

doughnut – a motor vehicle trick in which the driver rotates the front of the vehicle around the rear set of wheels in a continuous motion

three-point turn – a method of turning a vehicle round in a narrow space by moving forwards, backwards and forwards again in a sequence of arcs

CHAPTER 7

NASCAR MEETS TRUCKS

In 2015 American racing fans saw something they hadn't seen for 15 years. Truck racing returned to a track in New Jersey. The event drew a crowd eager to see the huge racing machines.

Fans had the chance to see the trucks up close before the races began. The trucks were new, but many fans knew the drivers. Behind the wheel of every truck was a **NASCAR** driver. Drivers were competing for points that would place them in a championship at the end of the year.

The races began with a rumble. The trucks sped down the track at 161 km (100 miles) per hour, impressing onlookers and NASCAR drivers alike. The race made it official – truck racing in the United States was back and better than ever!

NASCAR – the National Association for Stock Car Auto Racing, the governing body of stock car racing in the United States

WILD! In addition to the costs of maintaining trucks, drivers must pay an entry fee in order to race. For the FIA ETRC the fee is €4,600 (about £3,900) for the season, or €1,100 (about £940) for a single race.

Racing trucks look similar to most HGVs. They are generally 2.4 m (8 feet) tall, with no official limit on length.

CHAPTER 8

STORMY WEATHER

What do you picture when you imagine a day at the races? A sunny afternoon in the stands? Trucks flying by, glinting in the sun? That's not always the case. Truck races have been held under stormy skies too.

In 2015, one race weekend in Wales, drivers and fans were met with sheets of rain. This didn't stop the drivers of the BTRA Championship from heading out onto the track.

As they fought for a lead the trucks also fought to steer through pouring rain. Great waves of water sprayed up from their tyres. The slippery track sent trucks spinning into the grass. Mud and water sprayed everywhere. Many races were delayed as trucks and drivers were slowed by the wet conditions. The weekend marked the second-to-last weekend of racing in the championship. Luckily the drivers and trucks had three weeks to dry out before the final race.

Rain can delay truck racing for hours. Water on the track can make for slick driving conditions and unpredictable races.

CHAPTER 9

A RACING LEGACY

Jochen Hahn, driving truck number 3, began racing in 1996. He raced with his brother for one year. In 1998 he created his own team, called Team Hahn.

WILD!

Truck races start with a **rolling start**. This gives trucks a chance to warm up with a cautionary lap before the flag is dropped and the race begins.

Jochen Hahn knows that every race is important. This German truck racing legend has been behind the wheel of a truck since the 1990s. Some races, though, are truly unique.

Jochen Hahn

In 2016 Hahn entered the FIA ETRC. The championship took place over a long weekend. For three days Hahn was dominant on the track. He was winning and pushing past his competition. On the third day of the championship, he started a race from the second row. But he did not stay behind for long. Hahn was right behind the leader in the first turn. As he raced to catch up, the leading truck's engine began to fail. A plume of smoke erupted from it. Hahn saw his chance. He quickly moved into first place. When he crossed the finish line he did more than win a single race. He had won his 100th race. This officially put him among the very best truck race drivers in Europe.

rolling start – when trucks begin on the track with laps at a predetermined safe speed before accelerating

CHAPTER 10

MAKING HISTORY

New ground is broken in truck racing every year. More drivers are joining the sport than ever before. This includes Steffi Halm and Ellen Lohr. In 2016 the two were racing to the be the first woman to win a major truck race.

In 2016 Halm and Lohr entered the final race of the season at the Le Mans circuit in France. While these women competed against each other, they were also on the same team. Racing teams join together and share points to win championships. Lohr quickly moved into first place when the race began. Halm was on her tail straightaway. The two women may be teammates, but neither gave way to the other. Halm was able to race past Lohr just in time to win the race. Lohr came second. It was the first time two women stood together on the winner's podium.

www.truckrace.o

44

Steffi HALM

Steffi Halm began racing in 1993. When she is not racing trucks, her favourite activities include watching motor sports and playing handball.

Halm was delighted by the result of the 2016 Le Mans race, saying "It was fantastic for me to win the last race of the 2016 season. But to finish 1 and 2 together with my WOW – Women On Wheels – teammate Ellen, two girls in the first two positions and making history with that result is just incredible. All I can say about that is WOW!"

GLOSSARY

articulated lorry a truck consisting of a cab and a trailer

debut a first showing

doughnut a motor vehicle trick in which the driver rotates the front of the vehicle around the rear set of wheels in a continuous motion

heavy goods vehicle (HGV) a large, heavy motor vehicle used for transporting goods

infield the area in the center of a racetrack oval

inspect to look at something carefully

plume a long cloud of smoke or vapour resembling a feather

rolling start when trucks begin on the track with laps at a predetermined safe speed before accelerating

three-point turn a method of turning a vehicle round in a narrow space by moving forwards, backwards and forwards again in a sequence of arcs

NASCAR the National Association for Stock Car Auto Racing, the governing body of stock car racing in the United States

FIND OUT MORE

Monster Mega Trucks ... And Other Four-Wheeled Creatures, Tim Kaine (Triumph Books, 2014)

Mud Truck Racing: Tearing it Up (Dirt and Destruction Sports Zone), Brian Howell (21st Century, 2014)

NASCAR Racing (Checkered Flag), Paul Challen (PowerKids Press, 2015)

WEBSITES

http://www.fiaetrc.com/

http://btra.co.uk/

http://truckraceusa.com/

http://race-trucks.com/

http://www.btrc.co

INDEX